DISCOVER DG GRAPHICS

RUMPELSTILTSKIN

WRITTEN BY STEPHANIE PETERS

ILLUSTRATED BY FORREST BURDETT

raintree

a Capstone company — publishers for children

Raintree is an imprint of Capstone Global Library Limited, a company incorporated in England and Wales having its registered office at 264 Banbury Road, Oxford, OX2 7DY – Registered company number: 6695582

www.raintree.co.uk
myorders@raintree.co.uk

Designed by Kay Fraser
Original illustrations © Capstone Global Library Limited 2022
Originated by Capstone Global Library Ltd
Printed and bound in India

978 1 3982 3411 6 (hardback)
978 1 3982 3721 6 (paperback

British Library Cataloguing in Publication Data
A full catalogue record for this book is available from the British Library.

WORDS TO KNOW

brag talk in a boastful way about yourself or someone else

dungeon prison, usually underground

miller person who grinds grain into flour

straw dry plant stems

CAST OF CHARACTERS

The **miller** brags about his daughter. He says she can turn straw into gold.

The **daughter** gives Rumpelstiltskin whatever he asks. In return, he spins the straw into gold.

The **king** asks the miller's daughter to spin straw into gold.

Rumpelstiltskin can spin straw into gold. He demands many things from the daughter, including her firstborn child.

HOW TO READ A GRAPHIC NOVEL

Graphic novels are easy to read. Boxes called panels show you how to follow the story. Look at the panels from left to right and top to bottom.

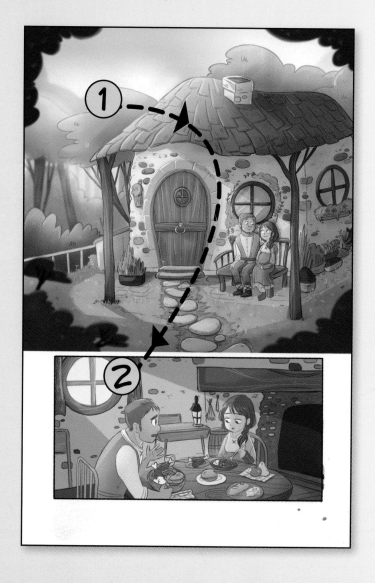

Read the word boxes and word balloons from left to right as well. Don't forget the sound and action words in the pictures.

The pictures and the words work together to tell the whole story.

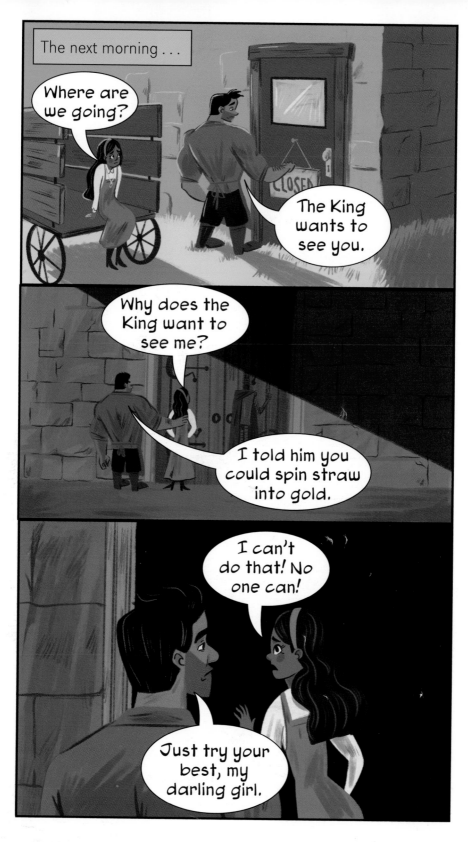

8

13

17

The next morning . . .

Amazing! I have all the gold I'll ever need!

I did my best.

And you will be a queen.

I will!

The King and the miller's daughter were married that very night.

21

27

WRITING PROMPTS

1. Rumpelstiltskin is an unusual name. If you could change your name, what would you change it to? On your own or with an adult's help, write a list of five names. They can be silly or serious!

2. The king ends up with piles of gold. If you were him, what would you do with the gold? Write a paragraph describing what you would do with your riches.

3. The miller's daughter uses the word *short* to describe Rumpelstiltskin. What are some words that describe you? Write them down and circle the one that describes you the best!

DISCUSSION QUESTIONS

1. The miller brags that his daughter can spin straw into gold. Have you ever bragged about someone? Have you bragged about yourself? Talk to an adult about it.

2. The miller's daughter needs help to spin straw into gold. Can you describe a time you needed help to do something?

3. The miller's daughter puts on her old clothes before she searches for Rumpelstiltskin. Why do you think she did that?

PAPER PLATE PUPPETS

Would you like to put on your own puppet show about Rumpelstiltskin? These paper plate puppets can help you do that. They're easy to make with construction paper by cutting out eyes, noses, mouths and hair. Best of all, you can make the characters look however you want.

WHAT YOU NEED:

- craft glue
- craft sticks
- small paper plates
- scissors
- construction paper
- felt-tips, crayons or coloured pencils

WHAT TO DO:

1. Glue a craft stick onto a paper plate.

2. Cut out small circles from a piece of construction paper for the puppet's eyes.

3. Use a black felt-tip, crayon or pencil to colour a smaller circle inside each eye.

4. Glue the eyes to the front of the paper plate.

5. Cut out a small triangle from a piece of construction paper for the nose.

6. Use a black felt-tip, crayon or pencil to colour two small circles next to each other on the nose.

7. Glue the nose underneath the eyes on the front of the paper plate.

8. Cut out a big circle from a piece of construction paper for the mouth.

9. Fold the circle in half.

10. Glue the bottom half of the circle under the nose on the front of the paper plate. The top half should open upwards.

11. Cut a piece of construction paper into strips for the hair. The length of the strips will be the length of the hair.

12. Glue the strips around the top edge of the paper plate.

13. Decorate your puppets any way you want! Make a crown for the King. Give the miller's daughter extra-long hair. Rumpelstiltskin could have big, pointed ears!

READ ALL THE AMAZING
DISCOVER GRAPHICS BOOKS!